MINNOW AND THE BEAR

Ben Blathwayt

RED FOX

Minnow came home from the woods one day with sticks for the fire.

"You should not go so far alone," said the women in the cave.
"I'm always on my own," said Minnow. "The others go hunting without me."

"When you are bigger," said the women, "you can go with them."
Minnow was cross. Minnow ran to the magic cave.

"Is there a spell to make me big and strong?"
he whispered to the cave.

"Can I come too?" Minnow asked the hunters as they set off.
They laughed at him. "Bears and wolves will eat you up. Wait until you are stronger."

So Minnow watched them go.
Then he went down to the river to play.

He saw a huge fish swim into the fish trap!
I will be a real hunter if I can catch such a big fish, thought Minnow.

But he slipped and fell backwards into the deep river.
"Help!" he cried.

Minnow grabbed at branches and boulders as the river swept him on.

Then he crawled on top of a floating log and held on tight.

But what was that on the other end? It was a little bear!

All day they floated down the river,
Minnow and the bear together.

All day they drifted with the river,

far and far, and on and on.

At last the log ran aground on a little beach.
Minnow and the bear crawled ashore and fell asleep.

A cold wet nose woke Minnow in the morning.
The little bear was still there!

Nobody will ever find me here, thought Minnow. I have come such a long way.

Below their little beach the river spread out so wide and deep that Minnow and
the bear could go no further.

They looked for something to eat but couldn't find anything.

Then Minnow and the bear saw something amazing. . .
There were lots of big fish swimming upriver through the shallow water.

It was easy to catch one.
"Now I am a real hunter," laughed Minnow.

Minnow went back to their little beach and made a shelter.

Then he sat down and shared the fish with the bear. It was delicious!

"We will stay together," said Minnow, "and we will be friends."

The sun rose, the sun went down.
The days passed by, one by one.
And bit by bit
the boy and the bear
grew big and strong.

But one morning a cold wind blew.
The fish had vanished from the river.
And there was ice.
Minnow knew it was time to go home.
"If we follow the river back the way we came,"
he said, "then one day we will reach the
great waterfall and the caves beyond."

So Minnow followed the river upstream.
And the bear went too.

It was a difficult and dangerous journey;
but at last they reached the waterfall and
Minnow knew that he was nearly home.

As they climbed the cliff, a great storm began to blow. But what was that noise?
It came closer and closer.

It was a herd of bison! The storm had terrified them. One fell over the edge of the cliff.

Minnow and the bear were so cold.
"Look!" cried Minnow. "A tree has been struck by lightning. The fire will save us!"

Minnow and the bear slept safe and warm as the winter storm blew all around.

In the morning, the whole world was white with snow.
"Come on," said Minnow to the bear. "We are almost home."

"It's me!" cried Minnow when they reached the caves. "It's me, I'm home!"
But something was wrong. "What's the matter?" he asked.

"The hunters have been gone many days," said the women gloomily. "We have no food.
The storm blew out our fires."

"Don't worry," said Minnow. "Follow me!"

Minnow led them back to where the bison fell.

But when they reached the foot of the cliff, they couldn't find the bison anywhere. Perhaps he had imagined it all.

"But look!" The bear had found the bison under the snow.
"Minnow and the bear have saved us!" everyone shouted.

On the way back to the caves, Minnow found a few embers still glowing in
the ash of his campfire.

That night the hunters returned. They had found nothing.
Nothing at all.

"Don't hurt the bear!" said Minnow. "We are friends."

The women told them how Minnow had brought food and fire to the caves.

Later there was great feasting and storytelling. Minnow was a hero!
"You can come with us as often as you want," said the hunters to Minnow,
"but that bear will look after you wherever you go!"

So Minnow wandered far and wide,
never lonely, never scared,
the big strong bear
there at his side.